To Michael J. Heppen, C.S.C.

Quicumque alienaverit hunc librum A. S.

12-3-'80

Paul E. Beichner, C.S.C.

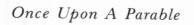

Once Upon A Parable

Once Upon A Parable

FABLES FOR THE PRESENT

with

Fifty-two hand-cut illustrations

by

PAUL E. BEICHNER

THE UNIVERSITY OF NOTRE DAME

NOTRE DAME, INDIANA

To

Theodore M. Hesburgh, C.S.C.

WOODCUT, 1961

Contents

PREFACE

Since the making of this little book of fables has been fun for me, I hope that others will find it entertaining. The idea of doing it occurred to me after Dr. A. L. Gabriel, then Director of the Mediaeval Institute, and I had been exchanging some choice medieval anecodotes as we walked across campus from a dull academic meeting two years ago.

Because I had been reading the parables and fables of Odo of Cheriton (+1247), as a start I loosely translated or adapted some medieval fables, giving each a new moral— often nothing more than a wisecrack. To several I added sequels, and then I wrote fables of my own, which constitute more than three quarters of those in this collection. The Aesopic character of a few of the fables will be recognizable because Odo used material which went back ultimately to the Latin prose "Romulus" reworking of the Phaedrus.

The final step was to put a hobby of mine to use and make cuts to go with most of the fables. These illustrations employ masses of black and white as well as some white lines on black and some black lines on white; they do not merely produce line drawings in black and white, as was the style of the woodcuts of Caxton's time.

The portrait of Father Hesburgh, President of the University of Notre Dame, to whom this book is dedicated, was cut on a little piece of wood a dozen years ago.

It is a pleasant obligation to thank Professor Richard T. Sullivan for reading the collection, friends for making suggestions for fables, and all those who gave me encouragement by laughing when a fable was read. My special thanks cannot lessen my debt of gratitude to Miss Emily Schossberger, who is an expert on all aspects of bookmaking, and who spent perhaps more time on this book than it deserves.

P.B.
Notre Dame, Indiana
August, 1974

The Sheep

Once a herd of sheep, brought up for the summer to the
high pastures in the San Juan Mountains, found life monotonous after several weeks. They grew used to the splen-
did scenery of the Rockies and a magnificent sunrise and
sunset every day. Besides, with so much good pasture
everywhere, they became fat while satiety killed their
appetite. "A sheep can eat no more than his fill," complained one, "so what we need is change." "What we need
is a charismatic leader to give us some purpose," asserted a
junior member of the flock who had never spent a summer
in the high meadows before. "Baa," said an old ram, "the
last fellow who thought he was a great charismatic leader
turned out to have the talents and the instincts of a Judas
goat. We did not follow him, and he finally had to get a
job at the stockyards in Omaha." "But there ought to be
room for charismatic rebellion," insisted the novice. "Im-
possible!" exclaimed the ram. "If we can't have a charismatic leader or a charismatic rebellion, at least I want to
follow a charismatic calendar," argued the young sheep.
"A charismatic calendar? That's Greek to me," said another sheep inquisitively, and for his enlightenment the
young one explained: "To follow a charismatic calendar is
to do *what* I damn please and *when* I want to." The
Basque shepherd's dog, who had been listening quietly to

13

the conversation, then spoke up: "Whether you fellows know it or not, I am your charismatic leader, endowed by nature and backed by the authority of the shepherd and of the Church and State. Now move, before that flock gets too far ahead of you."

MORAL: *Optimum conditions are delightful until they pall.*

or: *Call something "charismatic" and sheep follow it; there's magic in the word.*

The Trick of a Fox

A certain fox, when he was hungry, used to pretend that he was dead and lie beside the road with his tongue hanging out. A crow or a raven seeing the motionless fox would fly in to seize his tongue and would be seized and devoured instead.

MORAL: *Sneaky, but it's a living.*

SEQUEL: One day when he was very hungry, the fox tried his favorite trick. As he lay by the highway, an ambulance stopped, attendants threw a blanket around him, strapped him tight to a stretcher, and roared off to a hospital. There, in the confusion, the stretcher was sent to the basement, where he died of hunger in a room full of old blankets.

MORAL: *You can't get away with it forever.*

SEQUEL TO SEQUEL: The fox's girl friend down the road who tried the trick was a luckier lass. When a red sports car stopped, she no longer pretended but roared off with the driver to the beach; and the surfing was grand. He was a wolf.

MORAL: *Wolves don't discriminate against women.*

The Lemmings

One spring when the snow and ice began to disappear from the frozen tundra and stunted forests of the north, a couple of Canada Geese were forced to land because of bad weather. They were given hospitality by a colony of lemmings, and they spoke about the happenings in the south the previous summer and the rumors of still greater things to be expected during the coming summer. The lemmings became more than politely interested, when they explained about the wave of music festivals sweeping the U.S. "They are usually held in places with *Wood* in the name, like Woodstock, Wood Island, Woody Acres, and the like, and they last for a weekend or even a week. Young people travel hundreds of miles, live in the open, and put up with all kinds of inconveniences just to be there," said one goose. "You forgot the chief attraction," said the

other, "the rock groups, with names like the Roaring Rocks, the Bouncing Boulders, or the Stunning Stones. It's a kind of mass vacation or mass madness." When the weather cleared and the geese flew on north, the lemmings consulted other colonies of lemmings about going south and attending one rock festival after another. Soon millions of lemmings were on the march, consuming the grass before them. Fortunately they were turned back at the border because they had no visas, and thus the regular attendants of the rock festivals were not squeezed out.

MORAL: *Look out for lemmings.*

or: *Get your tickets early.*

or: *Stay at home.*

The Kite and the Partridges

A kite once sat in the top of a dead tree admiring himself. "What strong wings and legs and talons I have," he thought. "Am I not as well armed as a falcon or an eagle?" Then he noticed a covey of partridges scratching for food under the low trees a short distance away. "I'll blast them like the lightning that blasted this tree." He swooped to the attack, caught one in his beak, one under each wing, and one with each foot. Finding himself unable to move, he opened his mouth to curse and one escaped. This so startled him that he raised his wings and two more escaped. Thrown off balance, he tried to recover his footing and the two in his talons streaked to the safety of the thick brush.

MORAL: *Whoever takes more than he can handle loses all.*

18

The Beaver
and his Totem Poles

There was once a wealthy old beaver who carved totem
poles as a hobby. Although he had retired from a prosper-

ous business of building flood-control dams in the mountains for the state, he would still construct an elaborate swimming pool for a wealthy suburban client for a reasonable price if he liked the location and the water supply. But most of his time he spent planning and making totem poles. He even dreamed that he could turn a giant sequoia into a national monument as famous as the Washington Monument, with all of the presidents on it, if he had a sequoia. Some of the animals liked his totem poles, some did not, and some did not care because they thought he was a little bit odd. Some society folk said that his totem poles were truly great American beaver art, and some said that they were anti-art and eye-sores which ought to be hauled away to the paper factory for pulp. Anthropologists were not sure that the figures were totems at all, and theologians said that they were not inspired by the animistic spirit and that the beaver himself had no charisma, no prophetic sense, no social message, no talent whatsoever. Soon animals and birds noticed that they were being represented in various ways on different poles. Sometimes an animal wanted the beaver to touch up a detail or two to improve the figure representing himself. The beaver would climb up the pole to the place, and soon a few chips would come drifting down. On his return to the ground, he would be complimented by the critic who never noticed that this beaver always carried a mouthful of chips up the pole to drop at the proper time. To those who complained that they ought to be higher on the totem pole, he always responded: "The higher you are on the totem pole, the more the people notice your behind." The secret of the beaver's totem poles was revealed one day when his housekeeper, cleaning up his den, noticed the title on an old manuscript roll of birch bark, *Aesopic Fables.*

MORAL: *Ask the Forest Service to give him a sequoia. We want to see what he would do with the presidents.*

Nunc Pro Tunc

There was once a skunk upon whom old age and strange ideas had descended. To the annoyance of the community, if his opinions were not heard and followed, he raised a fuss. One spring day as he was crossing a swift stream on a slippery log, he lost his balance, fell in, and was swept away by the muddy current. He shouted for help and no one heard him until, exhausted and all but drowned, he was carried into a deep pool downstream where an otter was fishing for trout. "Help, help," he cried and went under for the third time. When the otter dove in and swam out to him, he panicked and tried to get on top of the otter. With a couple of smart chops to the ear and the neck the otter subdued him and towed him to the bank, where he quickly recovered. Two weeks later the skunk, charging the otter with aggravated assault and battery, had him brought to the animal court. To the charge the otter pleaded "Not guilty," and added that the only thing he was guilty of was the saving of a skunk's life. A couple of foxes, as counsels for the presecution and the defense, argued learnedly with each other to make up for the lack of witnesses until the judge, who was a black bear, grew tired and in order to get at the truth, he ordered everybody down to the bank of the stream for a reenactment of what had happened. When all were reassembled, remembering a Latin phrase which sounded legal the bear began: "This will now be a case of *nunc pro tunc*—Now for then. Mr. Skunk, kindly walk across the log and do whatever you did

on that day." Reluctantly the skunk started across the log and when he came to the slippery spot he became so flustered that he fell in, although he had not intended to. He came to the surface, spat out a mouthful of water and shouted: "Help, help!" "Now, Mr. Otter," said the judge, "dive in and rescue him." "Rescue him?" said the otter; "he maintained that I assaulted him and tried to drown him. If this is a case of *nunc pro tunc*, I'll not be a Good

Samaritan this time. Besides I pulled him out downstream around the bend." "Help, help," shouted the skunk; "the otter did rescue me downstream around the bend, but I can't last that long today." "Then the case against Mr. Otter is dismissed and this court is adjourned," said the bear. "Now, a couple of you beavers, guide this log out to Mr. Skunk when I roll it down the bank, and when he has climbed on, push it towards shore downstream so he can get off. I for one would not care to get as close to him as Mr. Otter did."

MORAL: *Be kind to Good Samaritans.*

or: *A skunk may be a stinker all his life.*

or: Nunc pro tunc, *if properly applied, sets things right.*

The Sensitivity Session

Once a few small forest animals, at the instigation of a pair of birds who had returned from the west coast, decided to form a sensitivity group. The birds said that sensitivity sessions would help the individual to learn what others thought about him, to understand himself better, to appreciate his dependency on others, and thus to increase the mutual respect and love for each other. And so the group met in a mossy glade, sat in a circle, and held paws for a while. Then the rabbit said to the skunk whose paw he held: "You stink, Sir, and are scarcely approachable." "You are right, of course," said the skunk, "but that's my defense when I don't want to be approached too closely. And you, Sir, are always scared, or you would not run and

try to hide so much." "That's my defense, too, when I don't want to be approached at all," replied the rabbit. And then he spoke to the porcupine on his left: "My friend, you are indeed a grumpy, bristly character. A person is afraid to shake hands with you, to say nothing of patting you on the back for fear of those sharp quills." The porcupine answered: "My quills are my defense when I don't want other animals pawing me." Then he said to the flying squirrel: "Squirrel, you are a nice but timorous little fellow. Others would like to know you better but you are always leaping from tree to tree or from branch to branch in the twilight." "That's my defense too," the squirrel replied, "lest larger animals get too close to me." "Now that we all understand each other much better," said the porcupine, "let's toss someone with a blanket so that he can appreciate his dependency on this group." "I volunteer," said the flying squirrel, thinking it would be fun. So they tossed him with the blanket and just as he reached an altitude of sixteen feet, a wolf came over the hill, barking: "Ho, what goes on here?" Not waiting to be caught in the blanket, the squirrel glided to the safety of one branch after another; the rabbit raced away at high speed; the porcupine raised his quills and waddled into the brush towards a large pine; and the skunk raised his tail and shouted over his shoulder at the wolf: "We were having a sensitivity session. How sensitive is your nose?"

MORAL: *Sensitivity sessions may be for the birds.*

or: *Too much closeness may become unbearable.*

or: *Don't let your defenses down when the wolf prowls.*

The Barbarians Are Coming

In a remote mountain valley there once lived a community of animals at peace, for they considered themselves civilized and cultured, and natural barriers served as their defense against the outside world. In the misty past an old mountain goat had dreamed that one day barbarians would come looking for gold and occupy their land. Because the dream was thought by some to be prophetic, each spring someone would start the rumor, "The barbarians are coming!" and it would spread from one animal to another until all were thoroughly frightened. A lordly elk, the prince of the animals, then would call his council and decide to do something further about defense. One year the national guard was doubled by inducing a few more mountain goats and bighorn sheep to come from other regions, live in the crags, and keep a lookout over the passes. Another year the civil air patrol was trippled by the addition of six more families of eagles. Then a buffalo was persuaded to get his five brothers to move up from the plains; they made a formidable cavalry if they charged together. Finally one spring day when the rumor got started that the barbarians were coming, although the eagles could observe no troop movements from the air, the prince and his advisers decided that nothing further could be done to repel an invasion. He therefore declared the next day a holiday on which all of the citizens were to turn out in their finery to welcome the barbarians. And this they did. Animals came down from the crags, in from the meadows, and up from their burrows; they strolled around the center of the valley, and greeted and talked to each other as well as the prince. Some were a little disappointed because they saw no barbarians but only their neighbors. Before the sun went down, the prince made a speech: "If the barbarians are coming, they are here already, but I would not call myself or any citizen a barbarian." So they lived at peace for many more decades. But the prophecy was fulfilled when men came into the valley with heavy equipment to mine for rare metals more valuable than gold.

MORAL: *Who decides who is a barbarian?*
or: *Xenophobia makes every stranger a barbarian.*

A Night at the Drive-in

Once a mule, a goat, and a dog decided to go to a
drive-in. Having no car and no money for admission, they

knew they had to be ingenious. They scouted the area carefully before the sun went down. The mule found a knoll where he could stand and look over the fence at the screen in comfort; the dog found a place where he could dig under the fence, but to do so would take time; and the goat discovered a low tree into which he could climb, but a branch spoiled his view of the screen. The mule solved the problem of the other two by offering to allow the goat to stand on his back if he would allow the dog to stand on his. The dog carried several hamburgers because he could not eat grass as the mule and goat had done. The night was pleasant and the breeze was cool, and John Wayne in "True Grit" outdid himself. During the middle of a shoot-out the dog decided to eat his hamburgers. As he bit down hard on a juicy one, catchup spurted out and fell on the forehead of the goat who, without thinking, raised a hoof to brush it away and rubbed some of it into his eye. As he bleated in pain, the pyramid came tumbling down. The mule stubbornly refused to allow the goat and dog to get up on his back again, while he watched John Wayne triumph over bad guys and evil to the end.

MORAL: *Small artists who stand on the shoulders of greater artists should not drip paint on their heads.*

The Child
and the Butterflies

Two swallowtails sailed gayly among the flowers and blossoms in the park, pausing now and then to rest or to

taste the nectar of a delicate bloom, until one had an accident. "Mummy! Mummy! Look at the pretty colored bird I caught," exclaimed the child in delight. "Put that filthy thing down. And don't eat it!" ordered Mummy.

MORAL: *Imagination is a powerful thing.*

or: *Beauty or filth often rests in the eye of the beholder.*

The Mice and the Catnip

A peasant once procured a large, crafty, and efficient cat to protect his cottage and barn from mice. But the mice called a town meeting to determine what they should do. An old historian among them reported that no mice had ever been able to hang a bell on a cat. One outdoor type suggested that they take to the fields and stay away from the buildings until the peasant decided that he had no need of a cat and would get rid of her. Another mouse said: "There is not enough time for that. She will probably have kittens in a couple of weeks and then it will be too late to do anything." When the chairmouse called for further observations, one mouse said that whenever the cat walked by a patch of mint near the garden, she always acted very strangely. "Yes," added another, "she seems to become intoxicated, or to have cat fits and ecstasies, as though she had been using pot." "That mint must be catnip," said another. The chairmouse replied: "Then we must make the most of it to discredit her in the eyes of the peasant at once. We must dig a burrow in the center of the patch with many escape tunnels." The burrow was completed in one night and the plan was tried the next day. A couple of mice enticed the cat to charge after them into the catnip, where the aroma of crushed leaves sent the cat into an ecstasy of sheer delight as she rolled about. After a while she wandered away as though in a dream. Then the mice took to rolling in the crushed leaves and rubbing

30

themselves with them. Even when the cat was minding her own business, they would parade close to her so that she could not avoid the aroma of catnip or the sight of them but would go into an ecstasy of pleasure. Finally the peasant noticed the odd behavior of his cat whenever she saw a mouse, and thinking she must be insane, he got rid of her.

MORAL: *A good perfume makes a pussycat purr.*

Three Catalpa Worms

Early one summer morning three catalpa worms awoke and began to eat the leaf on which they had spent the night. "Now take it easy, Harry. You don't need to try to

eat all the leaves on this branch in one day." "Mind your own affairs, George. I'll do what I please." And he ate like a sawmill. "You idiot, Harry! Get away from the stem," said Herb, who was a good deal smaller. But it was too late because just then Harry bit through the fibers of the stem; the leaf tore loose from the twig and sailed out over the lake. The three hung on desperately until their leaf settled on the water and began to drift with the breeze. "Now if we don't panic, we will be safe," said George, "for the wind will blow this leaf to the bank and then we can get off." So they stayed quiet until Harry became hungry and began to eat the edge of the leaf. When he refused to stop, the others decided to fast no longer, and their lifeboat became smaller and smaller. Once a dragonfly stopped for a few seconds to investigate and then buzzed off. By the middle of the afternoon the three were huddled together in the bottom of what remained of their boat. "I'm hungry," said Harry. "But there is nothing more to eat," said Herb. "Oh! yes there is," said Harry, as he ate a hole in the bottom of the boat before the others could stop him. A bass ate the three of them when the water closed over their heads.

MORAL: *There is a time to feast and a time to fast.*
or: *Don't scuttle your boat by overeating.*

The Peasant and his Oxen

In the foothills of the southern Alps, where life was hard for both man and beast, a peasant eked out a frugal existence on a small stony farm. A yoke of oxen assisted him in his labors. But they grew resentful of all the work and mumbled to each other when hitched to the plow or the cart: "This slave driver makes us do all the work, takes for himself the best of all that grows, and beats us when we object to pulling that heavy cart. We ought to report him to the prince, or to the Department of Agriculture, or to the IFOO (Italian Federation of Oxen)." One day after the peasant had loaded up the dung cart in their shed, they

threatened to strike. The peasant took his dung fork, stood in front of them, and said: "Amici! Who fill-ed up your nice-a house with this-a stuff in the first-a place? Now move, or I'll-a beat some more of it out of you." The oxen looked at each other and said: "He's right, of course-a, and he'll do it." And they followed him out of the shed, pulling the dung cart behind them.

MORAL: *When you're full of it, keep your mouth shut.*

Grandfather Wolf

Once an aged wolf, his son, and grandson lived in a rundown home in the rocks in the deep forest. Grandmother Wolf had died many years before from lead poisoning contracted on a visit to the sheep pasture, and Mrs. Wolf had gone to stay that winter with relatives in Canada. Grandfather Wolf spent most of his time in the living room, which was the warmest room in the house. But he got on his son's nerves because he was so untidy, and in the long winter evenings he would cough and blow his nose during all the T.V. programs. His son finally gave him an old sheepskin coat and made him stay in his room, where he shivered and stared at the wall instead of the T.V., and he finally died of the cold. Several weeks later, when little Loupee was busily nailing the old sheepskin to the wall, his father said: "Son, what are you doing with that dirty old sheepskin?" "I'm saving it," he replied. "I saw you make Grandpa wear it, and I suppose I'll need it for you when you get old."

35

Do Clams Have Feet?

"Do clams have feet?" a raccoon once asked a beaver. "I don't know; I never paid much attention," said the beaver. "But when you were building dams, you must have seen whether clams have feet," insisted the raccoon. "I saw that frogs have feet and no shell, and turtles have feet and a shell, and a crayfish has feet and pincers and a shell. I don't like seafood, so I never paid any attention to clams. Why are you so interested?" said the beaver. "Well, there are a lot of them out there in the lake about thirty feet from shore; and if I bring some in and put them on the bank, I want to know whether they will walk away and get back into the water again," answered the raccoon. "Why don't you bring one out and see what happens," advised the beaver. When this was done, the two sat down and waited for the clam to start walking, but nothing happened. "Are you sure it's a clam and not a stone?" asked the beaver. "Sure, I'm sure," said the raccoon. "I still see no feet," said the beaver, "but I have to go now. Let me know what you find out." After the raccoon had waited a while longer and nothing happened, he went back into a marsh to catch frogs. A gull that had been watching the shore flew in, snatched up the clam, carried it aloft, dropped it on a large boulder, cracked the shell, and ate it up. That evening the raccoon and the beaver searched the spot where the clam had been placed. "It's gone," said the raccoon. "Then clams must have feet," said the beaver.

MORAL: *For a change, it is nice to be right for the wrong reasons, rather than to have all the right reasons and still be wrong.*

or: *It makes little difference to the owner whether something walks off by itself or somebody walks off with it.*

The Crows
and the Mourning Dove

Once, as a young mourning dove was playing jacks with some seeds in the yard, a sinister crow snatched the child and carried her away to his nest. The mother dove went to the pad of the crow and his slovenly girl friend and pleaded for the return of the chick unharmed. "Do you know how to sing?" asked the crow. "I know a little, but I am not very good," answered the mourning dove. "Then sing!" said the crow with a coarse oath. The dove sang as well as she knew how, but her song was full of oo's and ooo-ooo's; besides, she was frightened and pretty well broken up, for she had caught a glimpse of her baby bird gagged and tied up in a corner. "Stop the moaning and sing better, or you will never see your child again," ordered the crow, while his callous lady friend added with a smirk: "Even I could sing better than that." "I can't, I can't," moaned the dove. "I don't know how." "Then I will not release your little moaner," retorted the crow. The crows then drove the mourning dove away and devoured the little one. News of the affair came to Eagle, who exclaimed: "What's the country coming to?" He stopped soaring in the clouds, and made a sudden raid on the pad of the crows. They both sang like canaries, and the eagle drove them out of the country.

MORAL: *"I'd like to teach the world to sing in perfect harmony."*

or: *Call the F.B.I.*

The Trout, the Crayfish, and the Polliwog

"My name is Trout. And who are you?" the brook trout asked the first of the two creatures on the bottom of the pool. "My name is Crayfish," he replied. "Crayfish! Why, you are not a fish at all. If you knew any French, you would surely know that your family name was Crevice for hundreds of years, and more recently Écrevisse on the Continent," said the trout who was so smart. Then turning to the other he said: "Fat boy, what's your name?" "My name is Polliwog," was the reply. "Indeed? You are nothing but a roly-poly little frog." "And you, Sir Trout, are a lout!" exclaimed the polliwog. In spite of his learning the brook trout was caught that day by a little boy whose name he did not know.

MORAL: *In the mouth of a snob your name becomes an insult.*

or: *Apologies are more acceptable than etymologies.*

The Polar Bears
and the Penguins

Once a polar bear stared at a group of newly arrived penguins at the zoo and said in disbelief to his wife: "I can't believe it! Look at the crazy clowns who have moved into the embassy next to ours. They look like a bunch of musicians from a third-class symphony who have forgotten their instruments." "They look like nice people," replied his wife, "but I'll ask where they come from." She chatted for a while over the fence with a lady who was strolling around and she learned that they had come from a very cold country of ice and snow, surrounded by a sea of ice water, ice cubes, and icebergs, where the nights are so long that the days never come for months on end. "I still don't believe it," said the polar bear. "I know all the people from Greenland and Baffin Island to the Bering Sea. I have seen arctic foxes, the seals and walruses too, lemmings, the caribou and reindeer also, wolves, snowy owls, and huskies of Eskimos. And these folk dress different than any Russians I've seen, and besides, they're a little too small. I have never seen such people before!" "They say there are no people like us in their land either, but they like fish," said his wife. "Then they can't be all bad," he replied, relenting a little. "They must be from outer space," he said. "Yes, that's it—little men from Mars or Venus, or Neptune perhaps, because there must be fish out there. What do you

think, my dear?" "It has become a very small cosmos indeed," she replied, "ever since you started identifying all U.F.O.'s."

MORAL: *Don't confuse me with facts, for my mind is made up.*

or: *There are no penguins at the North Pole and no polar bears at the South, and no poles at either.*

Guido's Stags

In a forest park surrounded by a very high fence on his large estate in the Northwoods Guido kept some stags. They were magnificent creatures who could tear saplings to shreds as they rubbed their antlers against trunk and branches to remove the itching velvet. One day when several hikers came to look at them, the largest charged up to the fence, stopped, and put his nose through an opening. A hiker gave him a cigarette, which he ate with relish, and then another, and another. After mooching all the cigarettes which the hikers had, the stag pranced away and rejoined his companion, who said: "I thought that the Surgeon General has determined that cigarettes are dangerous to your health." "Only if you smoke them," the stag replied; "he said nothing about eating them."

MORAL: *To give up smoking cigarettes, try eating them instead.*

Watchdog

A family who lived in the suburbs procured a dog as a pet for their children. He was large, well mannered, and very gentle, and when the children played outside, he was always with them. On such occasions when he met other dogs of the neighborhood, who were all much smaller than himself, he told them that he was a watchdog whose job it was to protect the children from kidnappers and the house and property from thieves. Because of his size none of the

other dogs ever questioned his statements, and in time he began to believe that he was really a very good watchdog who merely tolerated playing with children, although he was fond of them. One day when the family went to visit relatives and left him locked inside the house, thieves broke in, kidnapped him, and stole the T.V. set. But the family had both insured against theft.

MORAL: *Understand your job specifications.*

Mutiny at the Hennery

Once in midwinter when life was monotonous in the hen house, one of the hens tried to start a rebellion. "Our rights are being trampled on every day by that chauvinistic chicken farmer," she said with feeling. "Why do we put up with these conditions? He never considers our wishes or our happiness. He thinks of us as mere egg-laying machines. We are worse than slaves. In the words of Patricia Henry, 'Give me liberty or give me death!' " One old hen said: "If you keep on protesting, you may get your second option." Another less wise said: "If we were united, we could overpower the farmer when he opens the door, smother him in our feathers, and then escape." "Escape where?" said another. "Have you looked out a window recently? There's more than a foot of snow on the ground!" "Things are not too bad here," said still another, "for he has provided our apartment building with electric lights, heat, and water. The food may be monotonous, but I overheard him muttering something about feeding us LAY-OR-BUST, and I, for one, would rather lay than bust." Another added: "As he wrote down the score for this building in his book yesterday, he must have been thinking of calling in the army because he said that if production did not go up soon, he would speak to a colonel at a Kentucky-fried-chicken establishment. We don't want to make our position worse." And so the rebellion subsided and by Easter time the egg production was high.

MORAL: *There is nothing to be gained from resentment. (Sirach)*
  or: *Cheerfulness prolongs your days. (Sirach)*
  or: *Whistle while you work. (The Seven Dwarfs)*

The Drones

A swarm of wild honeybees once lived in a hollow tree near an atomic power plant. Because a rumor had started that the bees had been exposed to too much radiation, a group of drones sitting outside in the sun buzzed with excitement. They argued vehemently with each other and tried to persuade anyone who would listen that the present administration had to be changed. "Only a stupid queen would have chosen this dying old tree near the power plant as the site for a hive," said one fat old drone, "but what can you expect when she and her council never tell us a thing about what is going on." "There must be tapes of their meetings in there," said another, "and if we could get them and listen to them, we could prove how corrupt this government is." "If I were king, I would do things differently. How I would like to order that female army of amazons around," added another. "If you were king!" exclaimed still another, "don't make me laugh." And when he laughed like a mini-sawmill, the other felt insulted and began to fight. They were all engaged in a stingerless brawl when an alarm sounded somewhere inside the hollow tree. A company of fighter amazons rushed out and finished off the mutinous drones, for the queen and her council had just decided that they were expendable.

MORAL: *Buzz off, when you can't change things anyhow.*

44

Three Not-So-Blind Mice

Once in early winter, as the sun was going down at the edge of the desert, three pocket mice were gleaning in a field. One said to the others: "We'd better finish soon, for it may get pretty cold tonight." Soon a burro, goaded on by a man in a poncho and carrying a lady bundled in shawls, came down the path. The boldest of the mice said to the burro: "Peace to you, and to all who dwell in these fields." The burro merely snorted and plodded on. The travelers turned in at an abandoned abode hut, sometimes used as a stable for sheep and goats. It did get very cold that night, and the pocket mice crept silently toward the hut. Light came from inside, and the soft humming of a lullaby. The mice paused near the door, and on a flat stone the first laid down a golden grain of wheat, the second a kernel of Indian corn, and the third a shiny cactus seed. Then they crept off to their burrow lined with dry warm grass, thinking they were three kings.

MORAL: *Gloria in excelsis Deo, et in terra pax hominibus.*

The Frog and the Bull

A bullfrog on a lily pad in the pond once saw the bull strolling around in the meadow in triumph. The frog was envious and thought how grand it would be if he were as big as the bull. Calling his sons he pointed towards the bull and said: "What size! What magnificence! If I can, I will try to become as big as that bull." He took a deep breath and blew himself up as much as he could. Then he said to his boys: "Am I now as big as the bull?" "Pop, you are not yet as big as his head," said the boys, feeling a little afraid. "Then I must inflate myself more," said the frog. He tried harder and harder and grew bigger and bigger until he went "pop." The bull glanced around and thought another bubble had burst on the pond.

MORAL: *Inflation is terrible these days.*

The Beaver's Book

There was once a beaver who became chairman of the board of The Small Lakes Dredge and Dam Company. The business meetings which he conducted were models of

brevity because his remarks were short, he made no long speeches, and other members began to imitate his example. Nevertheless, he always did much prior planning, thought a great deal, and listened carefully to others. As a highly respected member of the community he was much sought after to serve on boards and committees of all kinds of civic and philanthropic groups. Then he wrote a small book, *How to Hold Meetings,* in which he said: "As a young lumberjack, cutting down birch and poplar trees with my teeth, I soon learned that the more I talked the less I got done. The lesson was reinforced when I worked under water repairing dams: if I kept bobbing up to say something, the job took twice as long. Take it from me, when you work like a beaver, you talk very little and make no long speeches while you go about doing your job." Copies of his book were even purchased by a university for distribution to faculty and administration where committee meetings seemed to be taking too much of everybody's time.

MORAL: *Get a copy.*

The Alligator

Deep in the Everglades there once lived an old alligator who used to spend most of the day lying on a mud bank like an old log. He would doze for hours with his eyes closed and his mouth open, hoping that some frightened creature would seek refuge in his cavernous maw. Of late his reactions had become very slow, and by the time he could rouse himself from his slumbers and concentrate, the creature would have discovered his error and fled. Sometimes it seemed to him that his mouth became so dry that his jaws might remain locked open forever. Then he discovered that if he touched his tongue with his foot, the saliva would flow and soon his jaws would work again as quick as a steel trap. One day he came out of the water, lay on the bank with his mouth open, and immediately fell asleep. In his confused dreams he thought that a creature had entered his mouth. His jaws snapped shut over it, and he awoke with a start to discover that he had bit off his foot.

MORAL: *If you put your foot in your mouth, don't compound the mistake.*

The Dog Who Thought
He Was People

There was once a retriever named Brutus, who lived on a desolate tract of land in the north country which was good for nothing but hunting, fishing, swimming, and bird-watching. He was a magnificent beast, a long-distance runner and powerful swimmer. Because the decrepit dachshund there, who could scarcely step over a straw, was a poor excuse for a dog or for anything but a door mat, Brutus was lonely and developed problems. He began to think he was people, and to prove he was right, whenever rare visitors came, he would engage in a tug-of-war with someone for a log of firewood to demonstrate his strength, pull a floating oar out of the lake to show his intelligence, bark joyfully and smile, or do almost anything except argue philosophy. When no visitors were there, Brutus would survey his domain on foot, counting deer, sniffing for bears, exploring the swamps, and listening to the lonely coyotes bark on the ridges. One day in his travels he met a porcupine and engaged it in mortal combat. On returning home with his face and feet full of porcupine quills, Brutus received tender loving care from the caretaker who treated him like people, carefully removing all the quills with pliers. After several miserable days he recovered his enthusiasm and went exploring again. When he met a porcupine on the road that morning, he attacked again without thinking. Again he received a face full of quills for his stupidity, and again he received t.l.c. and hospitalization like people. The third and fourth porcupines which he met he thought were the ghosts of the previous two and that he could bite through them and they would disappear. They did not. But at least the attention he received during his hospitalization comforted his ego in spite of the pain. On his fifth hike he met a smaller creature, who instead of facing him and fighting like a man, turned tail and let him have it. Brutus took little satisfaction in having demolished him. On the way home he met no porcupines or other creatures for the breezes carried advance notice of his coming. Although he considered his case an emergency, he was turned away coldly by the caretaker before he could get into the hospital in the woodshop. As he turned away sadly to go alone and soak himself in the swamp, he concluded that, although he made as many mistakes as people, he might not be people, for they could always get emergency treatment in the hospital.

MORAL: *To live in people houses, stay out of the doghouse.*

The Mud Turtle
and the Eagle

A mud turtle, tired of seeing nothing but his low damp surroundings, once asked an eagle to carry him high in the sky because he wished to see the fields, the hills, the forest, and the mountains. The eagle agreed, carried the

turtle aloft, and after some time announced to his passen-
ger: "On the right side you will see the mountains and on
the left side the valleys and forests." "I can see them very
well indeed," replied the turtle, "but I prefer to be in my
swamp." To this lack of appreciation the eagle responded:
"Then you have seen enough," and let him drop. The
turtle cracked up in rough terrain.

MORAL: *Fly me to Cuba.*

The Crayfish
and the Polliwog

An athletic crayfish once undertook to train a polliwog who lived in the same pool in the brook. "First of all you must exercise those little feet and legs of yours," said the crayfish. "They are so weak you can't walk on them. See, mine are lean and hard and tough. Then, you must reduce, for you are much too fat and flabby." "But I have a good tail, and I can go like a torpedo," said the polliwog. "Like a torpedo out of control, stirring up the mud on the bottom," replied the crayfish. After several weeks the polliwog noticed that his feet and legs were getting bigger and they helped a little in his swimming, but he was not reducing at all. "Practice swimming backwards," said the crayfish, "because that will strengthen your stomach muscles, and you will become lean and hard like me." "But I can't swim backwards," said the polliwog, "and I hope I never get pincers like yours." "They are my karate hands," said the crayfish. "I can break things with them, or use them defensively or offensively." A robber raccoon came to the pool, put a paw carefully into the water and allowed the crayfish to attack and seize it with his pincers. Then he quickly lifted the crayfish out of the water to the bank and ate him up. The polliwog went like a torpedo out of control, stirring up the mud, and escaped under a rock. He grew up to become a mighty bullfrog, who was always fat.

MORAL: *The best defense is not always offense but escape.*

or: *The career of an athletic coach is often short.*

The Prairie Dogs

An old prairie dog town had developed into an urban sprawl without any city planning. Some of the more important prairie dogs-about-town complained that their streets were full of potholes and they did not even have a

decent road to other prairie dog towns in the county. They repeatedly talked to the town council, which said that it would do what it could, but did nothing. Then one year the state highway department cut a swath through their town with bulldozers and built a new highway. The chief prairie dogs-about-town complained to the town council: "You did not need to divide the town into halves with such a big road. Now it's worth your life to try to cross it when all those cars and trucks roar through." The town council said that it would do what it could about the traffic on the road, but did nothing.

MORAL: *What you get from the government you pay for, though it may not be what you want.*

Survival Training

Once an opossum was giving survival training to her young. She taught them how to hide, how to climb trees, and how to swing by their tails in the branches. As they made a tour through the orchard, she told them that berries and cherries, and plums and pears are good to eat. "But the most important thing is to know how to 'play possum' if there is no time to run from danger," she said, "because most animals will not attack something dead." Just then they heard a dog coming through the tall grass, so she sent the little ones up a tree to hide while she went off a short distance to play dead. Soon the dog reached the tree, sniffed around a bit, and then saw the pile of whitish yellow fur. In several bounds he was there and began to sniff at the pretending opossum. When he had his snout close to the white face, the opossum suddenly came to life and bit his nose like a black plum. With a howl of pain and surprise, the dog jerked away and ran as though all the demons of the woods were chasing him. When the little ones were gathered up, the opossum said to them: "See, that's the way it should be done." "But I thought you said that most animals will not bother something dead," said one. "That's true, son; but that dog suspected that I was not dead."

MORAL: *A live fighter is more frightening than a dead one.*

The Monk
Parakeets

Two monk parakeets were sent by their superiors in Argentina to evangelize in the wilds of a zoo in the U.S.A. After an exhausting flight, they landed safely at JFK Airport and some kindhearted idiot left the door of their cage open. Since no one paid the least bit of attention to two strange monks, they set out to find the zoo on their own. They tried to get directions from a pigeon but he could understand neither their Spanish nor their pigeon English and they could not understand Brooklynese. After a futile attempt to speak to an alley cat and a stray mongrel, they gave up. "Perhaps the Lord does not want us to evangelize the natives of the zoo," said one. "That's it," replied the other. "I think we're intended by Providence to propagate the faith over the whole country." They flew off towards Rhode Island, and they propagated more than the faith. Within a few years there were monk parakeets all over the east coast. Park pigeons complained: "If they continue to come to the parks to live, there will be a severe housing shortage. They are worse than the starlings." Titmice reported from the field that large numbers were moving to the country. A special meeting of the Bureau of Birds and Beasts was called to determine what the nation should do. A dove said: "All the people love to have them around, and they even help them to build their nests." "I'm for war," replied a hawk. "And I am not even in favor of chicken war," retorted a hen. "Remember the large influx of English sparrows at the turn of the century," observed a very old barn owl. "That population problem solved itself when the people got automobiles. Let's wait and see what happens." His opinion prevailed, and they adjourned the meeting *sine die.*

MORAL: *Bring back real colts, pintos, mustangs, and mavericks.*

59

The Little Fox
with an Identity Crisis

"I wish someone could help us straighten out that boy," murmured the vixen as she sat down in front of her den. "Who? Who?" inquired the owl from his perch on a tree near by. "Why, our son Junior, of course. He is over there lolling on the rocks. We think he is going through an identity crisis because sometimes he says he will be a badger, or a woodchuck, or a gopher, or even a rabbit. He now wants to take a year off to visit Berkeley, L.A., or Acapulco to discover what it is he wants to do." "Mrs. Fox," replied the owl, "you need not fear. He already knows what he wants to do: travel! And as to an identity crisis—he knows quite well that he is a sly young fox, if he can outfox you."

MORAL: *Go east, young man.*

The Ass Who Took Sick

An ass often saw how the pig was fed crusts of bread, pottage, scraps, and similar byproducts of the kitchen and granary, and how he did no labor except to chew and sleep. The ass thought: "The pig has it made: he eats well and labors not at all, whereas I work all day and get little to eat. I will pretend that I am sick." He did so, and lay down in peace. His master goaded him, but he only moaned and refused to get up. The peasant said to his wife: "I believe our ass is sick." "If that is so," she replied, "let us give him some crusts and meal and bring him some water." The first day the ass ate sparingly, the next day more, the next day to satiety, and the fourth day enough to start him growing fat. Just as he was congratulating himself on having it made, the butcher came from the village with his knives and instruments. When the ass saw what he did to the pig, he was terrified, fearing what would happen to himself when he became fat enough. He jumped to his feet, went out of the stable, and danced in front of his master, who said to his wife: "I think our ass is completely cured." He was put to work again and was given little to eat, but he kept his good figure and died a good death at a ripe old age.

MORAL: *Reduce, before it is too late.*

The Walnut and the Hazel

One summer day a walnut tree and a hazelnut bush growing side by side had a debate. "I am much bigger than you are and I give shade to men and cattle," boasted the walnut. "But I give shade and cover to small beasts and nesting room to finches and songbirds," replied the hazel. The argument was interrupted when several surveyors sat down under the walnut tree and ate their lunch. One threw the remains of his sandwich to an unknown dog who sat begging under the hazel. When men and dog had gone, the debate went on during the afternoon. "I give good wood for statues and banisters and nice T.V. cabinets," said the walnut. The hazel felt a little depressed and said: "I give nuts!" The walnut retorted: "So do I; but who ever heard of black hazelnut icecream?" "My nuts are called filberts, and are named for St. Philbert," replied the hazel. "Besides, who ever heard of a girl with walnut eyes?" And so it went. A few weeks later a screaming chainsaw cut down the walnut and bulldozers uprooted its stump as well as the hazel. A new superhighway replaced them soon.

MORAL: *"Nuts" to both your houses.*

The Bighorns and the Hunter

Two bighorn sheep, nibbling on some shrubs high in the crags, noticed a cougar slowly making his way up the slopes of the mountain before he could notice them. The larger one said: "We must make that fellow go back down, for if we go much higher, we'll run out of mountain." "I wish I knew how," said the smaller one. "We must make him think that he is being hunted by a man; and we can do it if you will help," said the larger sheep. "We must pretend to fight, but it has to be good." They found a wide smooth ledge, and back out of the mountain lion's view they charged at each other from eight or ten paces. Head striking head sounded like the report of a rifle in the cold clean air. They backed off and did it again, and still once again. As they looked over the rim of the ledge, they saw the cougar bounding back down into the valley, and the smaller bighorn kicked a stone over the edge to hasten him on his way.

MORAL: *Two heads are better than one, although they are not cabbages or lettuce.*

The Midnight Plumber

One night a gray mouse gnawed a hole out from the inside of a partition where there were pipes and conduits, and small passageways to floors above and floors below. Sniffing the air deeply, he could detect no odor of cat but scents of mice and food in the room. "I'll ask the mice for permission," he thought as he shouted out. Then he heard a faint squeak in the distance, which he traced towards banks of cages connected with mazes and contraptions that a budding Rube Goldberg might have designed. "What are you doing behind bars?" he asked a white mouse with sleepy eyes. "It's not the jail but a lab," he replied with a laugh. "We are helping a student to get a degree, and if all goes well, he may give one to us because we are very fast learners." "May I have some of your food?" the gray mouse asked. "I would give you some if I could," the albino replied, "but I can't give you any because of the timing device. When I run through the maze at certain times of the day and pull handles and levers, I get a pellet or two from a hopper above. They are full of vitamins and minerals and are quite tasty too." "Though I may be a plumber," the gray mouse said, "I am a fast learner also, and I would rather do what I want than live behind bars." So he left the pale college mouse, climbed up to the shelf where boxes of pellets stood in a row, gnawed part of the back off of one, and proceeded to carry armloads of pellets back to his hole. While he worked, he said to himself: "I am not robbing my friend because they belong to the student, who will never miss them; and as a nice gesture I will push some through the bars of that jail before I leave." The next morning when the student could not figure out how the pile of mouse food got into the cage, he decided that something had gone wrong with his mechanisms.

MORAL: *Don't be a slave to a cage full of gadgets.*
or: *We need plumbers too to look after the pipes.*

The Pacifists

Trotting through the park one day a dog of no breeding came upon an equestrian statue of a Civil War hero. Walk-

ing around it, he surveyed it with a critical eye, and finally hoisting a rear leg he made his inscription on the base. As he turned away, he said: "That's what I think of war and the military establishment." A pigeon, flying over just then, made his mark on the dog, and said: "I am a dove myself, but I am more opposed to dogs than to bronze generals."

MORAL: *Polite protesters carry signs.*

The Centipede
and his Footwear

There was once a centipede who lived among the leaves and detritus on the forest floor of a national park. Because he paid no taxes and had little competition from other bugs and insects, he acquired immense wealth; and rather than store it away to rust and mold, he decided to enjoy it. He noticed that hikers, passing through the forest, wore boots or shoes. The cowboy boots and the climbing boots were attractive, but the hiking shoes, hush puppies, and even old tennis shoes looked more comfortable; all must once have been new and bright. "If boots and shoes can give pleasure and comfort to big bipeds, think of what they could do for me and all my feet," said the centipede to himself. "I'll spend half of my wealth on shoes and boots." So he purchased fifty pairs each of fifty different kinds of boots and fifty pairs each of fifty different kinds of shoes. They all looked nice in their boxes, but wearing them was a different matter. It took him so long to put on his shoes when he got out of bed that half the morning passed, and he had to start taking them off before sunset to be able to retire at his usual time. He also discovered that if he wore fifty pairs of boots, he could scarcely walk, and if he should stumble or trip with his forward feet, the domino effect passed down the row to the end. Finally he worked out a system of boots for the first, the middle, and the last pairs of feet, and a combination of hush puppies, tennis shoes, and light walking shoes for all other feet in between. He admired his footwear and often paraded around so other centipedes could notice and be impressed.

But he could not really run, and whenever he felt the earth tremble as man or beast passed by, he found that he almost automatically curled up in a ball and hugged his well-shod feet. "This is stupid," he thought, "for here I am protecting my boots and shoes when I ought to be running to protect myself." He also began to worry lest he get athlete's foot from wearing boots and shoes so much of the time. Finally he decided to go barefoot again and to look for a different way of displaying his wealth because

he saw his friends, the centipedes, admiring a visiting millipede who was wearing five hundred pairs of moccasins, all of them beaded or fringed.

MORAL: *A conspicuous spender, or dresser, is always outdone by another.*

or: *The wealthy worry either about keeping their wealth, or about what to do with it, or about what it does to them.*

The Fox and the Badger

Once an old lady fox, who lived in the valley, suffered eye trouble which impaired her vision. Since the badger was the herb doctor of the animals there, she promised him the usual fee to cure her. He agreed and started to make daily house calls. The old lady fox had many fine utensils and furnishings in her home, and every day after putting medicine in her eyes, the badger would steal a vessel, until the house was almost empty. After several weeks the sight of the old lady fox improved and she discovered her loss. When she refused to pay the badger his fee, he had her brought to court. Before the animals assembled in the grove near the spring, the old fox pleaded her case. She argued that she need not pay the badger the fee which she had promised because he had not effected the cure which he had promised. Her house, she said, was full of beautiful vessels and vases and utensils as all her neighbors knew, and now she could not see even a quarter of them. The badger dropped his claim to a fee for a cure.

MORAL: *After being robbed, don't be badgered.*

The Ants,
Crickets,
and Grasshoppers

A commune of ants, crickets, and hippie grasshoppers once had a picnic at the edge of an untilled field of an abandoned farm. After lunch, as the crickets sang and strummed on their guitars, a grasshopper and his girl put on a dance, leaping high in the air. When they stopped to rest, the grasshopper said: "When I was up there, I noticed some smoke drifting in our direction." "Oh, somebody must be burning some rubbish," replied a cricket. "But it doesn't smell like rubbish," said one ant, while another added, "It may start a grass fire," and a third advised, "Let's get out of here." "Oh, you ants all have hangups or neuroses on ecology and safety," said a grasshopper. "I'll admit it may not be rubbish," said the cricket, "for it smells a little too sweet." "It's not hay," said a grasshopper seriously. And to determine what it was, all the picnickers sniffed hard and long as heavier clouds of smoke billowed towards them. Soon they did not care what it was, and they all took a bad trip together. Then as the county sheriff's men continued to burn out the patch of weeds, a small grass fire licked out and blackened their picnic grounds.

MORAL: *Don't get caught near a marijuana patch. That grass ain't hay.*

The Two Dry Flies

Two flies sampled drinks from dirty glasses in a desert saloon. "I don't know why we come here," said the first to

the second. "The beer is bad and the wines are mush worse."
"We don't come here, stupid! We live here," retorted the
second. "Have you already forgotten that we barely made
it from the cab of the truck that stopped outside this joint
two weeks ago? We're stuck here now and can't get away."
"I'm almost shtuck in this glass, because my feet are so
heavy," replied the first, "but I could drink you under yon
table." "That stuff goes to your head as well as your feet.
Now try to walk it off," said the second. "The shtuff or
my head? Be speshific and less dogmatic," stammered the
first. And so they quarreled as they struggled out of the
glass and assisted each other to the front edge of the bar.
There they fell off, but they got their wings working in
time to make a soft landing at the base, where they
staggered into a crack. "I hope we don't get shtuck in this
crack and can move in the morning," said the second as he
passed out beside the first.

MORAL: *The stronger your drink, the weaker you get.*
or: *Wine is fine, but liquor is quicker.*
or: *Bar flies become alcoholics by chance or by choice.*

The Wolf
and the Fish Pond

One cold day a wolf met a fox trotting down the path
towards him and greeted him: "Where have you been,
brother?" "Oh, I've been fishing, and I ate so many I have

to jog now to work off my dinner.'' ''How do you catch them?'' asked the wolf. ''You go to the fish pond, put your tail down into the water, and wait very patiently. After a while the fish think that your tail is dead and something edible and they bite on it and cling to it. Merely pull them out on the bank and eat them.'' ''Do you think I could do it?'' asked the wolf. ''Certainly,'' replied the fox,

"for you are stronger than I am." The wolf went to the fish pond, sat down on a comfortable stone at the edge, let his tail down into the water, waited patiently, and fell asleep. Meanwhile the temperature dropped and ice formed on the pond. The wolf was aroused from his slumber by a tingling sensation in his tail, and he thought: "I know from the tingling that I have a great number of fish clinging to my tail." He tried to move, but his tail was frozen fast. After a howl or two he was arrested by a game warden for fishing without a license.

MORAL: *Go to Grandma's house for a nice warm dinner.*

or: *Pick up a T-V dinner at the supermarket.*

The Praying Mantis
and the Rose Bugs

Once a praying mantis was strolling around the rose garden as though in quiet meditation when he met a rose bug who had been casting a hungry eye at several buds on a tea rose bush. Having never seen a mantis before, the rose bug said: "Who are you?" "I am a visiting clergyman enjoying the beauty of the rose garden," the praying mantis replied. The rose bug then shouted to a companion: "There's a Jesus freak over here, or some Holy Joe, or some kind of praying nut. You ought to see him before he goes away, for you will never see anything half so funny today. He looks like a freak who escaped from a side show." The second rose bug joined the first, and slapping each other on the back, they both laughed like idiots at the grotesque form of the mantis. Showing no sign of being insulted, the praying mantis approached the rose bugs, and suddenly dropping his attitude of prayer, he seized them both and ate them up.

MORAL: *More things are accomplished by the prayer of a praying mantis than most folks dream of.*

The Lion's
Problem

Once a lion, the king of beasts in his underdeveloped country, wished to give a royal banquet to honor himself on his birthday. There were two parties in the little kingdom, the vegetarians and the non-vegetarians, and since this was to be an affair of state, he could not afford to offend either party. "It will be easy enough to provide fresh grasses, wild celery and lettuce, assorted grains, sugar cane, shoots, leaves, and fruits for the vegetarians," he thought, "and the non-vegetarians will not be offended by what is provided for the vegetarians. The problem will be to provide meat for the non-vegetarians. I can not have half of the menu look like half of the guest list." He summoned his head chef, who had studied his art in Paris, and placed the difficulty before him. "Zere is no problem," the chef replied. "Your guests know ze English tongue and not ze French, yes? So, ze menu will have ze vegetables and ze fruit dishes in ze English for ze vegetarians and ze meat dishes in ze French for (how you say?) ze un-vegetarians. If we import ze meats from other countries, not one of our animals will be reported missing." The banquet was a grand success: the menu for the non-vegetarians began with Venaison à Richard Coeur de Léon and included Cheval pour les Chiens and Mouton du Berger. All the animals were merry. The deer and the antelope, the zebras and wild asses, the goats and the sheep all read the menu and were not 'offended by what they did not understand.

MORAL: *Consult the chef; he may be a philosopher-statesman.*

or: *Know when to use French.*

or: *Try soybean imitation meats.*

77

The Snake
Who Liked Eggs

There was once a blacksnake who liked eggs so much that in the spring he gave up catching mice and beetles and dined solely on eggs. All the birds for miles around were worried sick because the blacksnake could find a nest in the bushes and trees as well as on the ground, and so they held a conference to determine what could be done. "That old snake is callous and cruel," said a mourning dove, and Old Crow replied: "Aw, he's just hungry and lazy." "I can understand how he is able to swallow an egg as small as mine," said a goldfinch, "but I don't see how he can swallow grouse eggs." "Aw!" said Old Crow, "he unhinges his lower jaw and inhales them; it's easy. But I think I can trick him if some of you birds will keep an eye on him for a few days and if others will report every snapping turtle seen."

Several days later, after a warm rain, a blackbird reported that a large snapper had come out of the swamp and was digging a hole in the moist sand at the edge of the road, and another scout said that the snake was sunning himself on a rock not far away. The crow flew to a branch above the snake and said: "Aw! Snake, wake up! It's time for lunch, and I will tell you where you can get the gourmet's delight if you will give me one of them." "Eggs?" inquired the snake. "Certainly! Chicken-of-the-sea eggs," replied the crow. "That old turtle yonder has rolled two dozen of them down that hole behind her, and they would be easy for you to swallow because they are as

round as ping-pong balls and their shells are soft and
rubbery. But be quiet and quick about it, before she fills up
the hole with dirt." The blacksnake followed the sugges-
tion, put his head down the hole, and started to swallow
an egg. Just then the turtle turned around, seized the snake
in her powerful jaws, pulled him out, bit him in two, and
then calmly filled up the hole with sand.

MORAL: *The gourmet's delight may be his downfall.*
or: *There is no truth in Old Crow.*

The Venal Woodchuck

There was once a woodchuck who, as justice of the peace, settled petty disputes and claims among the small animals in his neck of the woods. Although he did not seem to mind, it was whispered about that those who greased his palm would get a favorable decision. A simple old lady chipmunk was pestered by two pine squirrels who were trying to take over her blueberry bushes. When she went to the office of the woodchuck to make her complaint, he opened the door, extended his paw and said: "How are you, Mrs. Chipmunk? Please come in." She answered, "I am quite well for an old lady," and placed a patty of butter in his paw. "I found this little square of Meadow Gold after some picnickers left, and I thought it would make very good grease for your sore palms." The woodchuck was embarrassed and tried not to show it. "Excuse me a moment," he said, "while I put your welcome gift of medicine in the refrigerator, and then we can visit or get down to business." And he thought to himself: "Although I may be venal, she does not know it, but she would immediately notice if I were not a gentleman and gave offense."

MORAL: *Never embarrass a little old lady.*
or: *There is more than one way to grease a palm.*

Snow Bears

One night a bear went up the path to his home through the snow, singing Old Langsyne at the top of his voice. The hot honey wine which he had drunk with the boys at the bar had gone to his head and his heart. He thought it was rather nice of Brother Moose and Brother Elk to walk him as far as his gate. As he was fumbling with the knob of the front door, Mrs. Bear drew him inside, then quieted him down and got him to bed. The next morning she gave Cub a quick breakfast, bundled him up with mittens and muffler, and sent him out in the yard to play in the snow. She knew that her husband did not like to be disturbed when he had a chance to sleep late. Cub tramped out patterns and neat designs all over the back yard, then he jumped into the snowbanks near the back fence. In search of fresh snow he went to the front of the house. There, jumping from footprint to footprint, he went from right to left down the walk, from front door to street gate and back again, sometimes pausing to sit in the snow. When he reached the front door, Mrs. Bear drew him inside, brushed him down and said: "Cub, I told you to play in the back yard. What on earth were you doing in front of the house?" "Oh, I was playing Daddy when he comes home from town on Saturday nights."

The Coyote

Once a coyote who wanted to be a folk singer would spend nearly the whole night at practice. Climbing up to the rimrock overlooking the valley, he would sit down and go through his repertory, for he had composed many songs with runs of high yips and barks followed by long

soulful howls that made the spine tingle. Whether there
was a full moon or not, he spared neither his throat nor
the feelings of the neighbors. "What's wrong with the
coyote? Is he sick, or something?" asked the little jack
rabbits in their bed. "Yes, children, he is, in a way,"
replied their mother. "Put your paws over your ears and go
back to sleep." Other creatures, who talked about the
coyote during the day, all had their own theories. "Maybe
he thinks he makes the moon wax and wane by his

incantations," said an owl, "or makes the night go away and the sun rise in the morning." "I think he is lonesome," said a sly fox. "And he needs a girl friend," added a modest brown doe. "At any rate, he ought to travel as folk singers do," said a great antlered elk, "to win fame and acclaim in distant places. Mr. Fox, you are his relative and can tell him so." The valley had quiet when the coyote went away, and he gathered huge crowds wherever he went. He came back in two months to the rimrock above the valley and sang solos to the moon and to his girl friend when the two were not singing duets together. They performed for a week and then went away to distant places to win greater acclaim and make recordings.

MORAL: *A folk singer sounds great, except to the neighbors.*

The Mouse Who Thought He Could Fly

One rainy night Mouse, wet, cold, and hungry, discovered five or six pills which had fallen from several damaged cartons during delivery to the back of a drug store. He first sniffed and then licked the moisture which had collected on the coating of one of the pills, which he found sweet and nicely flavored. Several others seemed to be coated with gelatin. Having tested each, he lugged them to a cool, dry place. The exercise had made him warm, he had lost his appetitie, and he felt strange and light. He went home.

"I can fly," Mouse said to his wife, as he shook raindrops from his ears. "Yes, dear," she replied, "now where did you leave the groceries you went out to get?" Still mumbling to himself, "I can fly," he went out again to bring back the forgotten pieces of cookie and several peanuts which he had found and hidden before the pills. As he crept through an alley with his bundles, he noticed a bat clinging to the side of a building. He stopped and studied it. "Yes, I can fly," Mouse said to himself as the bat flew away, "and I even look much like him."

When at last Mouse arrived home, his wife said: "What kept you so long?" "I can fly," he piped, "do you want to see me?" "Not now, dear; you would need more space," she said, and after a moment she looked into his eyes and added: "you must be getting the flu; I think you should go to bed." Mouse meekly went to bed, thinking how liberating it was to be able to fly, and he dreamed about it all night. At breakfast all he said was: "I can fly; do you want to see me now?" "When the dishes are done, I will watch you," said his wife, humoring him.

When they later went outside, Mouse said: "I will climb up the trunk of the dogwood tree and start flying from one of the longest branches." "Yes, dear," replied his wife, "and I will watch you," thinking he would soon climb down. As he jubilantly scampered across the lawn and started to climb, his wife crept farther and farther away from the safety of their hole so that she could keep him in view as long as possible. By the time he had reached the second tier of branches, her concern for his welfare had made her unaware of Silent Paws, the cat, who pounced on her from behind. Mouse oblivious of everything climbed out on a long limb and jumped off. During his free-fall into a pile of grass and leaves he felt exhilarated and free of everything. Then he made his way back across the lawn, crawled into the entrance of his home, and called out: "I can fly! I can fly! Why didn't you wait to see me?"

MORAL: *Some folks are saved by their fantasies.*
or: *Not all "aspirins" are alike.*

Rabbits of the Runways

Once a pair of rabbits had to move because a new
shopping center was being built where they lived at the

edge of town. They consulted the real-estate experts, Gopher, Badger, and Woodchuck, about inexpensive home sites. Nothing was available except some land at the airport between the two longest runways. Gopher argued that it was a much better place to live than the golf course, where one had to dodge the golf balls of duffers even in the rough; Badger said that no dogs would disturb their peace; and Woodchuck promised that, although noise might be a problem for a few weeks, they would have plenty of lush grass for themselves. And so the rabbits moved. The first few weeks were the hardest, for when the big jets went down the runways, the rabbits were afraid that the roar of the motors would make their ears fall off, but they remained on their heads. Indeed the grass was good, and in due time they had a family, as rabbits do. Now, when the planes come down the runways, neither parents nor children raise their heads, for the ears of the parents have become numb to noise and the children were all born deaf.

MORAL: *It could happen to you.*
or: *Down with decibels.*
or: *Turn that Hi-Fi down!*

The Squirrel
and the Reporters

Late one sultry summer night when a severe thunder storm passed over the forest, a bolt of lightning struck a hollow oak tree, traveled down the side, and spent itself in the ground. Representatives of the forest media visited the scene at sunrise to take pictures of the damage and to interview the residents. A blackbird flew up to a branch near a door in the hollow tree from which a squirrel was

throwing some steaming leaves. Without apology he began:
"Mrs. Squirrel, I am from the *Muddy Current,* a paper with
many subscribers along the river front. Was anyone killed
in the accident?" The squirrel had scarcely said, "No,
but . . . ," when she was interrupted by a jay who
screamed: "I am from the *Blue Spruce Gazette,* which
serves the Conifer Hills community. How did you feel
when the lightning bolt struck?" As Mrs. Squirrel looked
past him in annoyance, a cowbird landed on the branch,

shouldered his way between his two competitors, and said: "I am from the *Yellow Grapevine,* which serves Grape Hollow. Mrs. Squirrel, I saw you throw some steaming leaves out the door. Was it hot inside?" Anger gave the squirrel courage to say: "You tactless, impertinent, unfeeling birds! My husband was severely burned, my children are still scared stiff, and I must get back to them. Now what do you really want? A replay of the storm?" And she slammed the door in their faces.

MORAL: *There ought to be a law . . .*

The Cat
and his Beautiful Wife

A certain Thomas, the cat, had a beautiful wife named Pretty Puss. She spent most of her time wandering around the village, visiting all the other cats of her acquaintance, for she liked to be seen and she despised Thomas in her heart because of his attitude on women's lib. One day a friend of Thomas, commiserating with him on the back steps, suggested: "Singe several spots on her pretty coat. She will be ashamed to be seen in it in public and will stay at home." Thomas followed this drastic advice, and Pretty Puss stayed at home and helped him catch mice all day. Missing her visit, her friends all came to serenade her from the back fence that night. Thomas could get no sleep and he longed for the day when the coat of Pretty Puss would grow back sleek and beautiful, and she could visit her friends or attend women's lib and PTA meetings as she wished.

MORAL: *Consult a Marriage Counselor. A person could die for lack of sleep.*

The Abbot,
The Abbot, The Abbot

Once upon a time there was an abbot who allowed his monks three dishes at meals. Dissatisfied, the monks met and agreed to pray the Lord that the abbot might quickly die. Whether because of these earnest prayers or because of something else the abbot died; but his successor allowed the monks only two dishes. The monks were very sad, held another meeting, and prayed for the quick demise of the second abbot. And the Lord took him away. His successor allowed them but one dish. At a house council meeting the angry monks almost had a unanimous vote on the motion that they should pray the Lord to take him too. One monk objected, saying: "I pray the Lord to give him long life and to hold him by the hand for our sake." In amazement the others asked, "Why?" He replied: "I see that the first was bad, the second was worse, and this one the worst; but I am afraid that when he dies an even worse one will succeed him and he will completely starve us to death."

MORAL: *Be happy with your Monks Bread.*

The Scarab Beetle

A scarab beetle once flew about among the flowering almond trees, through orchards in blossom, among roses, lilies and other flowers. Finally he threw himself down on a dunghill and there he found his wife who asked him where he had been. The scarab answered: "I have traveled the earth and flown over it. I have seen the flowers of the

89

almond trees, roses and lilies, but I have never seen such a pleasant and delightful place as this dunghill."

MORAL: *Whatever turns you on!*

The Seeing-Eye Dog

Once there was a German shepherd dog, a fuzzy thinker full of high ideals, who finished his schooling and had to choose a career. He wanted one in which he could find satisfaction helping people and thus fulfill himself and his destiny. "The career of a policeman has many drawbacks," he said to himself, "and I know I would get angry and bite anybody who calls me a 'pig.' Being a guard or a watchman at a warehouse is no life at all, but serving the blind might be a fine occupation." So he answered an ad for a seeing-eye dog and got the job. He lived with a master in several rooms where the shades were drawn most of the time, and sometimes there were strange odors and odd telephone calls. His master wore dark glasses and he wore a harness whenever they left the rooms to walk the streets or visit the park. Since there had never been a moment's hesitation when they crossed the street or boarded a bus, he began to suspect that his master could see as well as himself. One day as his master sat on a bench in the park and he lay at his feet, a stranger sat down and placed a small, news-paper-wrapped package between them. They talked for a few minutes while a policeman passed by, then the strang-er arose to go to a parked car. As he did so, he stepped on the dog's tail, who barked in pain, and the policeman looked back. The stranger muttered, "You pig," and started to run, but the dog thought that the insult was meant for himself and quickly caught him by the ankle and tripped him up. His master removed his glasses and ran the other way straight into the arms of another cop. The dog barked then at the package lest it be forgotten. Be-cause of his experience with odd odors, his destiny later called him to become a policeman in the narcotics division.

Moral: *When you help people, you risk being used.*

or: *Don't step on a dog's tail, for this may change his career.*

The Pack Rat
and his Art Exhibit

A pack rat who fancied himself an art collector once so filled his home and yard with all kinds of antiques and artifacts of nature that he could scarcely move around. Then, deciding to have a garage sale, he put up a sign and waited. Very few animals and birds stopped to buy, for they had all seen pretty pebbles, pine cones, and acorns before. "Perhaps I have been collecting the wrong kind of art," he thought; "I must be more discriminating and original." So when another pack rat offered him a few seeds for everything, he sold out and traveled down the mountain to the low country in search of greater art. As he surveyed a valley from an opening in the forest, he exclaimed "Eureka!" like Archimedes of the old world (or a Californian of the new), for there in front of him were several acres of twentieth-century artifacts. Some of these had four wheels and some had none; some were piled on top of others; some had glass windows and others no doors; some had crumpled fronts and others had crumpled rears. As the sun glinted on the chrome and windshields and the hoods of various colors, a couple of museum mechanics kept removing parts or rearranging the exhibit. The pack rat's mind boggled, but he knew what he would do. He returned home and during the summer months he set up a gallery of modern art in his front yard. It took many days to collect and almost as long to arrange all the pieces of metal sculpture to suit himself—three battered aluminum beer cans, a sardine can, pieces of copper wire, the necks of two broken bottles, some bottle caps, a red plastic drinking cup, four empty brass cartridges, and a pair of sunglasses with one lens. He was proud that his collection was not biodegradable and he would not sell a single object.

MORAL: *When you can't eat it, wear it, or ride it, it may be junk if you don't like it, or modern art if you do.*

The Kitten and the Mouse

An old cat once caught a mouse and gave it to her kitten. The mouse tried to escape but the kitten put its foot down on the mouse's tail and held it for a while, then allowing it to run for a few steps, it tossed it in the air and caught it again. When the kitten started the process over again, the mouse stood up on its hind legs, faced the kitten, and said: "If you want me to play with you, don't be so rough." "I am going to eat you," said the kitten. "I don't think I would be very tasty," replied the mouse, "for if I were, some company would already be producing mouse-flavored kitty food." "You may be right," said the kitten. "Let's play." "Tommy," said the old cat, who had been dozing as she rested, "it's bad enough to play with your food, but talking to it is worse."

MORAL: *All gourmets play with their food, especially with artichokes.*

or: *Cat food industries, you forgot one flavor!*

Those Fabulous
Frogs of Aesop

After a pair of beavers had once dammed up a small brook in the forest, frogs of all sizes and descriptions soon moved into the new pond from up stream and down stream, and from neighboring swamps and marshes. They were an unruly lot, who peeped or sang or bellowed all night. They disturbed each other's way of life and argued and quarreled. Finally they prayed to the Spirit of the Forest to send them a king to bring order into the community. By chance a large chunk of wood from a dead tree fell into the pond with a king-size splash. The frightened frogs dove to the bottom and waited to see what this king would do. He floated to the surface and drifted about in circles. After several days some of the frogs lost their fear and approached him with their petitions for better government. He did not react at all. At last an audacious bullfrog, climbing to the top of the piece of wood, bellowed "gloom-p, gloom-p" to clear his throat and addressed the assembly: "This is a do-nothing king who merely goes around in circles. He hasn't done a thing for us. I think

he's a blockhead." "Blockhead . . . blockhead," echoed the assembly and the shores. After the echoes died away, a very small peepfrog, who had acquired his education watching T.V. commercials, spoke up: "Let's ask Mother Nature to send us another king, if she is not too busy tasting butter." He had hardly finished speaking when a large water snake swam by and seized and swallowed two or three of the smallest frogs. The assembly immediately adjourned and dove to the bottom of the pond. When the mud had settled, a large bullfrog said to another: "Now there is a king who takes immediate action to keep those little pipsqueaks in their place." As the days passed, the water snake kept putting larger and larger frogs in their place, until even the largest of the bullfrogs considered him a tyrant or oriental despot and feared for their lives. But they could do nothing about it.

MORAL: *A blockhead is less dangerous than a slick snake.*

or: *It's not nice to taunt Mother Nature.*

The Dog and the Pancake

Once a stray dog, making his rounds of garbage cans, suddenly became very curious when he saw a piece of pancake moving slowly away from a garbage can. A number of flies were riding on it and others were hovering above. The dog put his foot down in front of it and said: "What's going on here?" An ant put his head out from under the pancake and replied: "We ants found this pancake first. It belongs to us, and my platoon is carrying it to our storehouse. Kindly move your foot to one side, Sir."

Then one of the flies spoke up: "We flies found this pancake first. It was the honey on it that attracted us, and it belongs to us." "I'll settle your dispute," announced the mongrel, and he ate the bit of pancake himself.

MORAL: *Every dispute has two sides, for it's a damn thin pancake that has only one side.*

The Buck and the Gnats

There was once an effete buck who could not stand gnats. The exquisite torture for him lasted several weeks every spring, for at that season when he walked through the undergrowth in the forest or in the grass and weeds by

the river, it seemed that gnats rose in clouds in front of his face, some getting into his nostrils and eyes and his ears. They didn't bite; they annoyed him. One day he asked his neighbors what to do. Some birds suggested that he eat the gnats which came too close and the others would get the message and depart. "But I can't do that," he objected, "because I am a vegetarian." "I could spray the area around you," said a skunk, "but no one would like it because that kind of insect repellent would be worse than the gnats." "You could stand in the river with your head above water," proposed a beaver, "or you could lie down in the mud at the shore." "Why did you choose this place to meet and talk with us?" inquired an owl. "Because there are fewer gnats here than elsewhere," the buck replied. "But you are wrong," retorted the owl. "You were too interested in us to notice all the gnats."

MORAL: *If you are disturbed by gnats before the eyes, thank God they are not imaginary.*

or: *Ignore minor annoyances and concentrate on world crises; it's more romantic.*

The Dog and the Bulrushes

It once happened that when a dog wished to do his rustic duty among a clump of bulrushes, one of the bulrushes spurred him hard on the behind. The dog retreated a distance and barked loudly at the bulrushes. The sharp rush said to the other bulrushes: "I much prefer that he bark at us from a distance than defile us at close range."

MORAL: *Pollution doesn't pay.*

100

The Cat
Who Became a Monk

In a certain refectory there was once a cat, who had
caught and killed all the mice except one magnificent
fellow named Rat because of his size. The cat, planning to

catch and devour him, shaved a tonsure, wore a cowl, made himself a monk, and sat and ate with the monks. Observing this change, Rat rejoiced for he believed he would no longer be in danger. He leaped and scurried hither and thither, while the dissimulating cat averted his eyes from such vanity. Having grown over-confident, Rat approached the cat, who suddenly extended his claws, seized Rat and held him fast. "Why the police brutality?" said Rat. "Why not let me go? Where is your Christian charity? Haven't you become a monk?" The cat replied: "With that kind of baiting, you will never get me to let you go, brother. When I wish, sometimes I appear like a monk, sometimes like a friar, sometimes like a canon, but I am always a cat." And he ate him up.

MORAL: *Never trust a fat cat.*

SEQUEL: After the commotion subsided, the monks caught the cat, defrocked him, and threw him into the fruit cellar for disturbing the peace.

MORAL: *Never blow your cover.*

The Lion, the Ass and his Son

The lion once held royal court at which his subjects presented requests for all kinds of favors. An ass brought his son and said: "Your Majesty, I would like you to do something to promote the career of my son." "And what does he want to do?" asked the lion. "He wants to go abroad to study foreign languages for he thinks that they would be useful to him," said the ass. "He has hopes of being employed abroad on important missions." The lion mused: "Foreign languages ... useful ... important missions?" Then as though inspired, he said: "I just recall how Burnell, that ass from Cremona, went to Paris and was dismissed from the university because he could not even learn French. No. I think it would be better for your son to bray at home than to prove to the world abroad what he is." Other animals in the audience hall overheard what was said by the lion and the ass. A goose remarked: "He must be stupid! Even little French kids speak French." A mockingbird replied with disdain: "I teach my nestlings

many exotic languages." And a fat pig merely grunted:
"He probably won't work."

MORAL: *Be smart. Study a computer language like
FORTRAN; you don't even need to speak it at home.*

The Confused Goat

One hot dry summer a goat was forced to look for
better pasture because the whole region was suffering from
a severe drought. He asked a pigeon how things looked
from the air. "Terrible," said the pigeon. "Everything is
parched." "Are there no green spots anywhere?" asked the
goat. "Why yes, at the university about five miles west,"
said the pigeon, "there are two very green fields; one is
inside the stadium, and the other, not far away, is surrounded by a fence. The fields are not being used at this
time of the year, and the grass looks lush." The goat found
the field, looked through the fence and saw that the grass
in the middle was indeed a lovely shade of green. When a
truck driver opened a gate to drive his load to a storage
shed, the goat slipped through and hid. He came out of
hiding when the truck left and the gate was closed, and he
found that the grass just inside the fence was parched as
dry as anything on the outside. "The center of the field
looks so much better," said the goat. "I'll try that." Too
late he discovered that plastic turf makes inedible grass and
that there was not even a dripping faucet where he could
soothe his parched throat. As he bleated for help, when
motorists sped down the highway, they merely remarked:
"The team must be getting a mascot like the Naval Acad-

emy this year." After a few days in this plastic pasture the gaunt goat was discovered, then taken to the dog pound where he lived on dry dog biscuits and water until he could be relocated at the Children's Zoo.

MORAL: *Never trust a pigeon to know good grass.*
or: *The greener stuff on the other side of the fence is not necessarily grass.*
or: *Better things for better living through chemistry?*

The Caterpillars and the Bowl

A nest of caterpillars once fell into a large bowl in the yard. They emerged from the nest helter-skelter and laboriously crawled up the inside of the bowl from all directions.

Not wishing to slide back down inside to the bottom and afraid of falling off the outside, each one thought: "I'll follow the leader, for he must know where he is going." For seven days they plodded forward, round and round. At last one said to the one in front of him: "Tell the leader to slow down. Pass the word forward." By the time the word had been passed along and had caught up to him from the rear, he was too dazed to remember that he had started it. And so for seven days they passed the word along as they crawled. Finally the heavens settled their problem; a heavy summer shower washed them all away.

MORAL: *Stupid are they who run around in circles, though they consider each other big wheels.*

The Ass Who Thought He Could Sing

Once the lion, the king of the beats, was troubled by periods of melancholy and depression like King Saul and he could get no sleep either night or day. He thought he would try to find a musician like David to soothe his moods with soft music and song. Runners were dispatched throughout the realm to proclaim the new position at court for the best singer in the land. An ass applied, saying that he had once worked for an Italian opera company but concealed the fact that he had only pulled the cart of a vendor of sweets outside the opera house. "We must have an audition," said the king. The ass took a deep breath, opened his mouth, and brayed horribly. "Stop!" roared the lion. "Your voice is terrible. Why did you lie to me? I

know that you would wake the dead from their sleep before ever helping me. Get out of my court."
MORAL: *It's better than the bagpipes.*
or: *Opera stars who are self-made seldom make it.*

The Toad and the Shoes

The animals once held a council to which a toad sent his son. But when the toad discovered that his son had forgotten his new shoes, he sought a swift animal who could hurry to the council with them. He hired a hare and paid his requested fee for delivering the new shoes to his son. The hare then asked: "How will I be able to recognize your son at the council?" "The most handsome animal at the council will be my son," replied the toad. "Does he look like a peacock or an ass?" inquired the hare. "Neither," replied the toad, "for a peacock has ugly feet and an ass has ridiculous ears. Whoever has a noble head like mine and a large chest and powerful legs and feet like mine will be my son." The hare delivered the shoes to the council and told the lion and the other beasts the manner in which the toad had commended his son above all other animals. The lion laughed and said: "To like a frog, one must be in a fog."

MORAL: *You can like anything if it is yours.*
or: *Look for the family resemblance.*

A Non-Violent Demonstration

In a small country which produced only oranges, lemons, bananas, and coffee beans, a mountain lion once ruled from seclusion as tight as that of Mr. Hughes. Indeed he was seldom seen. The sheep, the goats, the chickens, the monkeys, the parrots, and the rest of the citizens all felt oppressed. The reason may have been the stifling heat, but they accused the mountain lion of oppression. Rum-

blings of rebellion were heard in the forest, especially at night. Then one day a group of monkeys, attending the school of drama in the capital, decided to stage a demonstration the next day at two in front of the palace gates. They called the broadcasting stations and requested that carrier pigeons be sent to the school who could be shown the plans for the demonstration and the signs to be carried. On the six o'clock newscast the parrots repeated all that had been said by the students plus embellishments they

110

heard from each other. The lion, of course, heard the parrots prattle and scream, and he instructed three turtles in armor to be near the palace gates the next day by two. At the announced time the parrots and pigeons waited in shady trees to watch the demonstration. Nothing happened, nothing moved for more than two hours, not even the turtles in the shade of the wall. The next day at nine some parrots and parakeets went to the school to berate the monkeys. "You didn't show up for your own demonstration which you promised to hold," complained the chief speaker. "You have widened the credibility gap between broadcasters and the public." The monkeys practiced making faces as they sat in a group, until their spokesman said: "You boys put on a much better demonstration by announcing ours, so we took our siesta as usual at two."

MORAL: *Tell the media what you plan to do and you don't have to do a thing.*

The Porcupine with the Itchy Back

There was once a porcupine who was troubled with a very itchy back and he tried various ways to relieve the torment himself. When he rolled in the sand, the grass, and the leaves, he received no relief and he sometimes picked up leaves and mushrooms on the ends of his quills. He received some temporary relief when he could lean his back against a large pine and rub vigorously, but he nearly nailed himself to the trunk every time he tried it. Finally

he decided to seek the help of other animals. The fox, who was asked to scratch his back, thought that it must be a trick and refused. The porcupine waddled down to the edge of the lake to get a drink and there he asked an otter to scratch his back. But the otter laughed and said, "I never knew you were such a joker," and swam away to play with another otter in the lake. A loon, who was cruising by, overheard the conversation and suggested that he follow the path beside the channel to the next lake, where he might find another porcupine with an itchy back. This was not loony advice, for that is what happened; and the two porcupines had a wonderful time scratching each other's back.

MORAL: *Back scratching is best performed by two of a kind.*

or: Quid pro quo *in equal amounts.*

The Fox in the Hen House

A cold, hungry fox once came to the hen house and asked for admittance. "We will not open the door," said the hens. "You are our enemy and you always do us harm." "I will do you no injury; I swear it by God and all the Saints above," said the fox. "We don't believe you," answered the hens. "Would a dying man, about to meet his Maker, take such an oath if he did not mean it? Besides, if I perish from the cold, God will hold you responsible," argued the fox. Moved by piety, the Godfearing hens opened the door at last. The fox, quiet for a time, became warm, forgot his promise and his oath, caught and ate one hen, then another, and threw the whole hen house into confusion.

MORAL: *Those with a direct line to God think that* you *should pay their bill.*

or: *Hens should know that foxes are atheists.*

or: *Alas, hens are chicken-brained creatures.*

113

The Mouse, the Vat, and the Cat

A mouse once fell into a vat of wine fermenting in the cellar. The cat on patrol heard him squeaking as he tried to swim in the froth. "Why are you shouting?" asked the cat.

"Because I can't get out of this heady stuff," piped the mouse. "What reward will you give me if I rescue you?" "Anything you ask," gasped the mouse, with his mouth full of foam. "If I free you this one time," the cat bargained, "will you come to me when I call you?" "I swear I will," said the mouse, and crossing his heart he took a mighty oath. The cat pulled him out of the vat, dried him off, put him on the floor and let him go. Feeling hungry several days later, the cat went to the mouse's hole and called him to come to him. "I will not," replied the mouse from the safety of his hole. "But you took an oath that you would come when I called you," said the cat. "Brother," said the mouse, "I was drunk when I took that oath."

MORAL: *Don't call us. We'll call you.*

Kicking Order

Once an old crow, with a coarse display of name calling and anger, drove a catbird away from some tall oak trees where the crows preferred to sit and preen. Fuming with frustration, the catbird flew to the fruit trees near the garden, where a hummingbird was exploring for blossoms. "Get out of my orchard," said the catbird, "or I will tear you apart like a fat butterfly." "This orchard is as much mine as yours," retorted the hummingbird; but since he was too small to fight, he shifted gears from "hover" to "forward" and darted off to the hollyhocks and trumpet vines by the garden wall. A bumblebee was there already at work. "You are stealing my nectar," said the hummingbird. "Leave, or I will spear you with my long sharp bill."

115

After buzzing furiously in protest, the bumblebee flew off and found a wildflower weed with a cluster of tiny blooms at the top. To an ant, sunning herself among them, the bumblebee gave a warning: "Get out of there, or I will sting you to death." The reluctant ant moved down the

stem, driving her herd of six aphids and kicking them as they went, although they never understood why.

MORAL: *To ease frustration kick something beneath you.*

The Rain Maker

Once during a severe drought the creatures of the region held a council meeting to determine what should be done to relieve the shortage of water. The snakes proposed that

117

the horses haul water for everybody from a great river many miles away. The horses objected to the hauling but gave as their reason that the water was polluted. The birds said that present supplies would last longer if strictly rationed to three spoonfuls in the morning and four in the evening for every creature, but the large animals protested, saying it was not enough for them. The sheep suggested that woodchucks, badgers, and gophers dig new wells, and they in turn said that the snakes and salamanders should clean out the springs which had run dry. Everything proposed for action was vetoed by the group who would have to carry it out. Finally, a lowly centipede rose to his many feet and said: "It seems useless for this distinguished body to pass resolutions for those who are indifferent to them to carry out. We should stop thinking of jobs for each other to do. I therefore propose—but only as a recommendation—that God give us rain." The assembly could not very well object to something which none of them had to do, so they approved the recommendation unanimously and adjourned. That night the Lord was pleased to answer this odd community prayer by sending a downpour.

MORAL: *Resolutions should be directed to those who are willing and able.*

or: *You never notice its water until the spring runs dry.*

The Hen and her Ducks

A farmer once placed some duck eggs under a brood hen. She was a little concerned because they were so large,

118

and she became very uneasy when her neighbors all hatched little chicks and nothing seemed to be happening in the eggs on which she was sitting. Patiently she stayed

on the nest, although she worried whether she might be sitting on a batch of door knobs or billiard balls. In a few more days her brood hatched. They were a hardy, cheery, joyous bunch, with flat yellow bills and big feet, a little awkward and inclined to fall on their faces; and she thought they were beautiful. One day when they were a little older, she took them on a stroll in the grass near the pond. At the water's edge one of the ducklings saw a reflection of himself and he stepped in to investigate. Before he knew what was happening, he was swimming around gaily because it was easier than stumbling around in the grass. Soon the others joined him in the fun. The frantic hen rushed to the edge of the water, calling, "Come back! Come back!" and they all replied, "Quack! Quack!" and kept on swimming. When they became tired, they came back and she tucked them in under her wings to warm them up. Thereafter she worried a good deal about what they would be like when they became teenagers. After six weeks she had a nervous breakdown, but the farmer had a dozen ducks.

MORAL: *Don't worry when kids are geniuses.*

The Fawning Ass

An ass once noticed how the two dogs of a certain peasant raced out to welcome their master when he returned from the village. They barked several times, wagged their tails, put their paws on his knees, their noses to his hands, and received a warm pat on the head for their attention. The ass thought deep within himself: "If I fawn on the master a little, he will notice me too, and things will go much better for me. After all, I am twice as big as both those dogs put together." The next day when the peasant was at church and the dogs were watching over the sheep in the meadow, the ass thought that he would graze near

120

the cottage and protect the property. In due time the peasant returned. The ass brayed twice very loudly; then with his tail waving aloft, he rushed at his master, put his forehooves on his chest, his muzzle into his face, and knocked him over backwards into a puddle of water. The peasant scrambled to his feet, and calling on the Lord for strength he grabbed a club and beat the ass back into the stable.

MORAL: *If you don't know how to do it, don't try.*
or: *Flattery will get an ass nowhere.*

The Saint Bernard
and the Dachshund

Once a Saint Bernard discovered that he could open certain doors at a supermarket merely by standing on a square rubber mat in front of them. When the door opened, he would walk through and then go up and down the isles until some supervisor, realizing that the store had no K-9 patrol, would lead him to an exit where the door would open for him as though for a shopper. One day he persuaded a dachshund to go with him. "It's a lot of fun," he said. "The doors are automatic and they open by themselves when you stand on the rubber mat in front of them. If you stick close to me there will be no problem." They went to the supermarket and when the door opened, they walked through it side by side. The Saint Bernard strolled around as though he had charge of the place, while the dachshund paused to look at stacks of Chuck Wagon, Gravy Train, Ken-l Rations, Alpo, and assorted brands of dog and puppy chows. While he was determining whether the number of brands of dog food was as large as the number of detergents, he caught a glimpse of the Saint Bernard turning a corner several isles over. He hurried and saw him standing in front of an exit door which opened and closed when he had passed through. Racing through a maze of feet and carts, the dachshund stood on the mat in front of the door. But nothing happened. He waited a while, and then set up a howl until an attendant caught him by the collar and cast him outside. "What were you barking at?" asked the Saint Bernard. "At that stupid door," said the dachshund. "It would not obey me."

The Woodchuck
and the Skunk

A woodchuck once dug three burrows which he considered his summer houses, one under a large rock in the clover field, one under a stump near the farmer's cabbage patch, and one in the bank near the spring in the woods. He would sojourn for a few days at one and then move on to another, depending on the weather and his fancy. One day he went to the hole near the cabbage patch and found that a family of skunks had moved in. "This is my house, Mr. Skunk," he said. "We would like to borrow it for a few mights until we find a place of our own nearer the hen house," said the skunk. "We will not eat your cabbages." "I suppose that will be all right," said the woodchuck, and he went off to his cottage in the clover field. Several days later he returned, and said: "When are you going to move out of my house, Mr. Skunk?" "Why, this is my house! Do you want to try to evict us?" said the skunk, with his tail raised. "I don't think so," said the woodchuck, and he went to his hole in the woods where the shade was deep and the ferns were sweet.

MORAL: *What you lend to the mighty consider a gift.*
or: *You're lucky to get off so lightly.*

The Lion's Dream

While taking his royal siesta during the heat of the day, a lion once had a remarkable dream. Upon awakening he not only remembered the vivid details but he also became melancholy and perturbed every time he considered it. "My dream must have a special meaning, and my crown will never rest easy on my head until I find out what it is," he thought. "Three years ago if I had not heeded my dream about the seven lean antelopes devouring the seven fat antelopes, I would never have been able to warn the kingdom about the seven months of famine to come." He therefore called his council and said: "As I was taking my royal siesta in the heat of yesterday, I dreamed that my paws hurt and my claws loosened and came out, and then my jaws ached and one by one my teeth fell out. Explain the signification of my dream." A wild ass brayed to clear his throat and said: "King Lion, the dream means that your lesser and your greater warriors, in whom you trust, will all desert you." "You are predicting treason," roared the lion, "and for that you shall be executed! We will adjourn until after the execution tomorrow and then consider my dream again." The next day the fox was asked to speak first. "King Lion," he said, "your reign will be glorious and the longest in the annals of the kingdom. You will triumph over all your enemies, and your life will be so long that you will outlive all your generals and all your trusted counselors, including myself and all those here present." "Now that's what I like to hear," said the lion. "Let us adjourn to the royal banquet hall to celebrate."

MORAL: *Only an ass makes the truth sound worse than it is.*

The Rabbit and his Problem

There was once a rabbit who worried lest his large family become even larger. He tried to persuade his wife to take the pill, but she refused, saying: "The pill is a poisoned pellet such as farmers use to destroy rats." Then he decided he would have to live as a celibate with his wife. In time his home was blessed with six more little cottontails. Finally he made up his mind to do away with himself by hanging. He searched around until he found a snare which some farm boys had set in the woods; and as he was about to put his head into the noose, the thought occurred to him: "I might be hanging an innocent man." He went home and pondered the problem for several more days but he could never bring himself to try to persuade his wife, or anyone else, to go near the noose. Then as he was moping around in his private hide-away in the brambles, he heard two shotgun reports, and on looking out he saw a hunter pick up two large rabbits, and one of them was his wife.

MORAL: *Don't count your blessings by the half dozen.*